ROYAL
MUSEUMS
GREENWICH

Royal Observatory Greenwich

Souvenir Guide

First published in 2019 by the National Maritime Museum, Park Row, Greenwich, London SE10 9NF.

At the heart of the UNESCO World Heritage Site of Maritime Greenwich are the four
world-class attractions of Royal Museums Greenwich – the National Maritime Museum,
Cutty Sark, the Royal Observatory, and the Queen's House.

ISBN: 9781906367640
Text © National Maritime Museum, London, 2019
Text edited by Louise Devoy and Emily Akkermans
All images © National Maritime Museum with the exception of the following pages:
graphic p20 by Matt Windsor; p58 courtesy of the Maunder family;
p51 courtesy of BT Heritage & Archives, p40 reproduced by
kind permission of the Syndics of Cambridge University Library.

Designed by Louise Turpin
Printed and bound in the UK by CPI Colour Ltd
1 2 3 4 5 6 7 8 9 10

Contents

The South Site

The Meridian Observatory

Flamsteed House

Introduction

Welcome to the Royal Observatory, Greenwich. Founded to help improve navigation at sea, the Royal Observatory has since come to define time and place for the world. Its history and the work done here explain why the historic Prime Meridian of the World – longitude 000° 00′ 00″ – passes through Greenwich and why Greenwich Mean Time (GMT) is the basis of the international time zone system.

The initial work of the Observatory

The Royal Observatory was founded in 1675, when King Charles II signed a royal warrant appointing John Flamsteed as his 'astronomical observator' (later called Astronomer Royal) and charging him with 'rectifying the Tables of the Motions of the Heavens, and the places of the fixed Stars, so as to find out the so much desired Longitude of Places for perfecting the art of Navigation'. With new trade routes opening up between Europe, Asia, Africa and the Americas, improving navigation at sea had significant political and economic implications. Mathematicians had already devised two theories about measuring longitude at sea: one involved measuring the changing positions of the moons of Jupiter, while another relied on observations of the Moon, as measured and timed at two locations for comparison. Both techniques required the development of new observational instruments and astronomical data to convert these theories into practice. By 1676 the Observatory, designed by Christopher Wren and Robert Hooke, had been built in Greenwich, overlooking the River Thames. For the next century, successive Astronomers Royal and their assistants meticulously observed the stars to help improve star catalogues, culminating in the first edition of the *Nautical Almanac* for the year 1767. Combined with newly developed angle-measuring instruments and timekeepers specifically designed for use at sea, mariners could now use astronomical methods to determine their position at sea with much more accuracy than before. Over subsequent decades, the Observatory expanded its contribution to navigation by becoming a testing centre for marine timekeepers used by the Royal Navy. It also become renowned as a place for establishing and distributing time standards such as Greenwich Mean Time (GMT) via its time-ball signal, telegraph signals and finally radio time signals in the early 20th century.

A new era of scientific enquiry

By the mid-19th century, new technologies gave astronomers at Greenwich the opportunity to explore questions about the physical nature of the stars themselves, rather than simply viewing them as useful reference points for timekeeping and navigation. The astronomers started to photograph the sky by taking advantage of new telescope mounts that enabled them to track the stars and capture faint images over several hours. The technique of spectroscopy – splitting starlight through a prism – enabled them to determine the chemical composition of stars. The scientific remit of the Observatory also expanded beyond strictly astronomy with the construction of a wooden building that housed instruments used for measuring the Earth's magnetic field and local meteorological results. The Observatory site expanded southwards to accommodate the demand for new telescopes, offices and photographic facilities.

▼ *The Royal Observatory from Crooms Hill, about 1696.*

▲ *Erection of the dome to house the 28-inch telescope, 1893.*

By the 1930s, the number of staff had increased to over 60 people but it was becoming increasingly difficult to observe with conditions worsening due to air pollution, vibrations from local industry and electrical interference from the nearby railway line. After the Second World War, the Observatory was gradually moved 97 km south to the more rural location of Herstmonceux in East Sussex. The former Royal Observatory buildings in Greenwich then became part of the National Maritime Museum and were opened to the public in 1960.

The former domestic and working spaces on the north part of the site are now galleries exploring the Royal Observatory's history and role in the search for longitude and the histories of astronomy and timekeeping. On the South Site, our staff help visitors learn about the work of modern astronomers through the Weller Astronomy Galleries, workshops and classes for all ages and observing sessions, alongside exciting shows in the Peter Harrison Planetarium.

The Astronomer Royal

Ten Astronomers Royal lived and worked here during the period 1676–1948. Before the 19th century, each Astronomer Royal worked alone, with a single assistant, on the meticulous task of gathering observational data required by other astronomers and navigators at sea. As the centuries progressed, the Astronomers Royal were supported by a growing team of specialists who lived in the local area. Today, the Astronomer Royal is an honorary title awarded to an eminent astronomer who promotes astronomy both within government and the public sphere.

The Astronomers Royal

John Flamsteed 1675–1719
Compiled a catalogue of stars that was larger and more accurate than any so far produced.

Edmond Halley 1720–42
Famous for his work on comets and his support of Newton's book on gravitation, the *Principia Mathematica*.

James Bradley 1742–62
Discovered the Earth's wobble on its axis, proved that our planet moves through space and established a new Greenwich meridian.

Nathaniel Bliss 1762–64
Succeeded his friend James Bradley as Astronomer Royal but only lived for another two years.

Nevil Maskelyne 1764–1811
Focused his work on producing astronomical data for helping navigators determine their longitude at sea.

John Pond 1811–1835
An accomplished observer who replaced the Observatory's old equipment with better instruments. Also set up the Time-Ball.

George Biddell Airy 1835–1881
A keen innovator who designed new instruments and improved the distribution of accurate 'Greenwich time' for public services.

William Christie 1881–1910
An ambitious man who expanded the Observatory's work by introducing more buildings, instruments, staff and collaborative projects.

Frank Dyson 1910–33
Responsible for expanding the distribution of 'Greenwich time' via radio signals and for the organisation of solar-eclipse expeditions overseas.

Harold Spencer Jones 1933–55
The last Astronomer Royal to live in Flamsteed House. He oversaw the relocation of the Observatory to its country site at Herstmonceux, Sussex.

Women at Greenwich

Women have always played an important role at the Observatory, either as the wives of the Astronomers Royal or as astronomers and assistants in their own right. During the 1770s, for example, Mary Edwards worked from home in Shropshire with her husband John, receiving and reducing ('computing') astronomical data from Greenwich for the Nautical Almanac. The first female staff were recruited at the Observatory during the 1890s by the 8th Astronomer Royal, William Christie, who chose a group of four mathematics graduates known as 'lady computers'. Despite their name, the women did much more than just working on the astronomical data; they were fully trained in the use of the telescopes and photographic equipment with their names appearing in the observing rotas. After a few years, most of the women left to take on better paid jobs elsewhere. During the First World War, there were more opportunities for women to work at the Observatory as several male members of staff were called up for military service. This started a trend that gradually increased during subsequent decades.

▲ *One of the 'lady computers', Miss French, around 1930.*

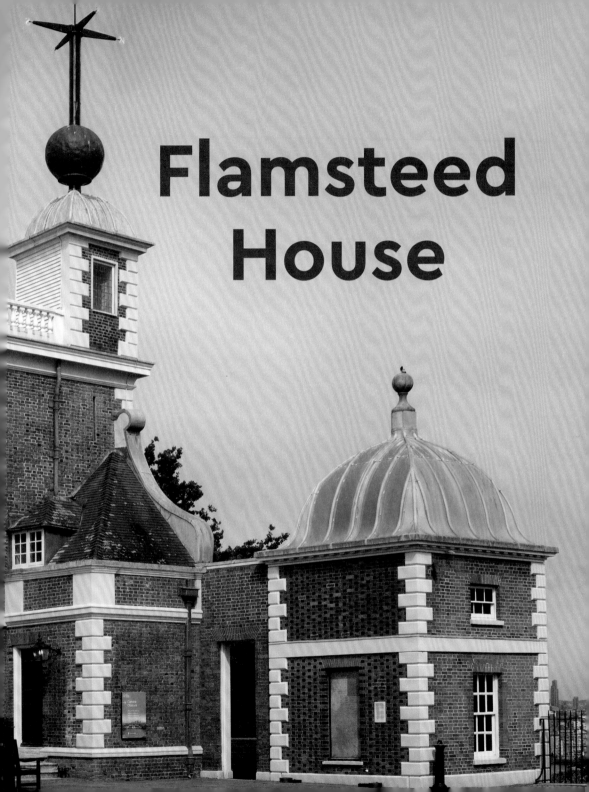

Flamsteed House

Named after the first Astronomer Royal, Flamsteed House is the oldest part of the site, originally designed by Christopher Wren and Robert Hooke 'for the Observator's habitation & a little for Pompe'. Various sites across London were considered but Wren's suggestion of using the ruined foundations of Greenwich Castle was quickly adopted. Situated on a hill with good views of the horizon, away from the smoky skies of central London, the rural location was ideal for observing but still accessible by river and road. Wren and Hooke had already gained much architectural experience from rebuilding London's churches after the Great Fire of 1666. The budget of £500 for the construction of the Observatory came from the sale of spoilt gunpowder and other savings were made by using recycled building materials from local forts. The foundation stone was laid on 10 August 1675 and the red brickwork structure began to take shape. Flamsteed and his two assistants moved into the ground floor 'dwelling rooms' in July 1676, starting their observations a few months later in the 'Star Chamber' (now the Octagon Room) above.

A century later, the cramped living quarters were extended southwards by Flamsteed's successors, James Bradley and Nevil Maskelyne, to create a bedroom, dining room and study, with a new kitchen in the basement. By the 1840s, Flamsteed House was extended further with more bedrooms to accommodate George Biddell Airy's growing family and a drawing room to receive guests. The building was much neglected after the

Second World War as the astronomers began the process of moving the Observatory down to Herstmonceux. In the 1950s, the ground floor of Flamsteed House was converted into accommodation for naval officers and the Octagon Room upstairs was opened to the public in May 1953.

▶ *Portrait of Flamsteed House, by Thomas Hosmer Shepherd and Rudolph Ackermann, 1824.*

▼ *A panorama of the Tudor and Stuart palace complex at Greenwich in 1637, from the top of Greenwich Park. To the left stands Greenwich Castle, a former hunting lodge that was in ruins by the time Wren suggested it as a site for the Observatory.*

Observatory Life

Explore the 'Observatory Life' rooms to discover more about two Astronomers Royal and their families, the Maskelynes (18th century) and the Airys (19th century).

The Maskelyne family

In the 18th century, Flamsteed House was a home, workplace and social hub for the 5th Astronomer Royal, Nevil Maskelyne, who first arrived at Greenwich in 1765. After living alone at Flamsteed House for almost 20 years, Maskelyne met Sophia Rose at a cousin's wedding. Within a month the couple were married, and a year later Margaret was born. Maskelyne took a keen interest in Margaret's upbringing. He kept detailed notes of key stages in her development, as well as recording periods of childhood illnesses and the remedies used to cure them. Maskelyne's notebooks also reveal how the family enjoyed entertaining guests such as local friends and relatives, scientific-instrument makers, other astronomers and scholars. Dinner guests could expect to enjoy fashionable foods served with fortified wines and exotic teas.

▶ *Portrait of Margaret Maskelyne, 1795.*

▼ *Portrait of Sophia Maskelyne, 1800.*

The Airy family

In 1835, the 7th Astronomer Royal George Biddell Airy arrived at Flamsteed House with his wife Richarda and their three young children. Six more children were born over the following years and the house was expanded with additional bedrooms for the growing family. Airy enjoyed being surrounded by his large family, and his wife Richarda gave him much moral and practical support such as accompanying him to public events, hosting guests at the Observatory and providing the illustrations for his books and lectures. As Astronomer Royal, Airy was called upon to advise on many scientific projects such as new railway lines, bridges, public clocks and lighthouses, for which he received many official gifts and honours. Extended trips to the country and holidays abroad gave the family some respite when Airy's workload became too heavy.

▲ *The Airy family.*　▼ *The Airy nursery.*

▲ *The Octagon Room, shown today and from an engraving made by Francis Place in 1676. The engraving shows John Flamsteed and his two assistants at work.*

The Octagon Room

When John Flamsteed, the 1st Astronomer Royal, arrived at the newly built observatory in 1676 there were no instruments, so he had to provide his own telescopes and clocks to measure the positions of the stars. He persuaded his patron, Sir Jonas Moore, to pay for several accurate clocks to be supplied by Thomas Tompion (1639–1713), London's leading clockmaker of the day. Their highly accurate 13-ft (4 m) long pendulums were concealed behind the Octagon Room's wooden panelling that was painted to look like expensive walnut. To maintain accuracy, Tompion designed these clocks to be wound only once a year, unlike most clocks that required winding every eight days.

Despite the Octagon Room's grand design, it was never used by Flamsteed for his work in creating a star catalogue to help improve navigation. By choosing to rebuild on the foundations of the former castle, the architects had created an observatory building that was not aligned with the local meridian (north-south line) and was unsuitable for measuring star positions. Flamsteed continued to use the Octagon Room for observing specific events such as comets and eclipses but the majority of his work was done in a purpose-built structure nearby.

The Camera Obscura

Situated in one of the former summerhouses, the camera obscura
(Latin: 'darkened room') is a functional reminder of how astronomers
and artists tried to capture images before the age of photography.
Daylight enters a small aperture on the roof, bouncing off a tilted mirror
into a lens and is focused onto a table below. On clear days, you can see
a projection of the Queen's House, along with a steady stream of cars,
buses and pedestrians moving along Romney Road. If you're lucky, you
might even catch a glimpse of the fast-moving river bus!

A camera obscura was originally installed at the Observatory to
help astronomers safely observe the Sun. The 1st Astronomer Royal,

▼ *A view of the city of London, as seen from the camera obscura on
the roof of the Royal Observatory, attributed to Edward Pugh, 1809.*

John Flamsteed, recorded this event on 2 July 1684: 'I observed the eclipse of the Sun ... on a scene [screen] in a darkened room'. The device was soon removed after Flamsteed's death in 1719 but nearly 60 years later, the 5th Astronomer Royal, Nevil Maskelyne, installed a new camera obscura in the western turret of Flamsteed House, possibly as an amusement for his daughter Margaret who was a keen amateur artist. The current camera obscura was installed in 1994.

◀ The building housing the camera obscura, as seen from the Meridian courtyard.

▼ An illustration of a camera obscura from Rees' Cyclopaedia, 1819.

The 'Time and Longitude' Gallery

Seafarers have always needed to know where they are to make a successful voyage. As European vessels undertook longer routes from the 15th century onwards, navigational accuracy – being able to pinpoint a ship's position on a reliable chart – became a pressing concern. Before the development of more advanced techniques, navigators plotted a ship's movements by measuring speed with a log-and-line and heading with a magnetic compass, then used these to recalculate the ship's position. This technique of 'dead reckoning' was generally successful, but could lead to errors, especially over long distances and in unknown waters. Famously, for example, British Commodore George Anson's ship *Centurion* was almost wrecked when its officers found they were over 300 miles east of their estimated position and perilously close to land after making the notoriously stormy and dangerous passage around Cape Horn in 1741.

◀ *Replica of a log-and-line, an instrument that was invented in the 16th century for measuring a ship's speed, 1961.*

▶ *Mariner's compass, by William Farmer, London, about 1750.*

19 ■

What is longitude?

One way of plotting your position on Earth is to imagine a grid spread over its surface, with the horizontal lines giving north-south position, or latitude, and the vertical ones east-west position, or longitude. Sailors can navigate according to this grid. Latitude is fairly easy to measure by observing the angle of the Sun or Pole Star above the horizon to indicate your position relative to the equator. Measuring longitude is much more difficult, especially at sea. Ancient Greek mathematicians realised that a difference in longitude is equivalent to the difference in time between two places, as measured locally using the Sun. As the Earth rotates once on its axis every 24 hours, every hour's difference in local time equals 15 degrees of longitude (360 degrees ÷ 24 hours = 15).

Line of longitude Line of latitude
75°
60°
45°
● Position 37°N, 60°E
30°
37°
15°N
60°
45°
30°
75°
15°W 60°
30° 45°
15°E 30° 45°
0°
Greenwich
Prime Meridian
Equator

▲ *Latitude and longitude are measured in degrees from the centre of the Earth.*

Longitude rewards

The determination of longitude has always been of great importance to nations investing in long-distance trade and settlements overseas. It is no coincidence, therefore, that offers of rewards for longitude schemes followed the sequence of maritime ascendancy of different nations.

The first incentive scheme was established in 1567 by King Philip II of Spain, the leading maritime power of the 16th century, and extended by his successor, Philip III, in 1598. The reward was never paid out but some promising inventions were recognised by the repayment of expenses. A Dutch scheme began in 1600, establishing a range of rewards that increased over time: 3,000 guilders in 1601, rising to 50,000 in 1738. As with the Spanish reward, many ideas and solutions were offered and a number underwent sea trial but none proved sufficiently successful.

England and France came relatively late to longitude investigations. Their governments and royal patrons invested in promising projects while their learned societies championed the establishment of observatories in Paris (1667) and Greenwich (1675) to provide the necessary astronomical data.

In July 1714, the British Parliament passed the first Longitude Act. This offered rewards of up to £20,000 (over £2.5 million today) for a practical method of determining longitude at sea, subject to certain criteria and trials. The Act created a group of Commissioners (later called the Board of Longitude) to judge claims and encourage invention. Nonetheless, many people still believed that finding the longitude was as unlikely as discovering the secret of perpetual motion or eternal life.

▶ Printed copy of the Longitude Act of 1714.

◀ *Set in Bedlam mental asylum (Bethlem Hospital), this scene shows one of the inmates sketching longitude schemes on the back wall. From 'The Rake's Progress', Plate 8, engraved by H. Hernell, after William Hogarth, 1735.*

Seamen, astronomers, inventors and artisans across Europe attempted to solve these problems for generations, attracted by the lure of large financial rewards. Sea-clocks and other new inventions went on sea trials but failed. In the end, however, the rewards offered under the British Longitude Act of 1714 bore fruit with the successful development of two methods. One was the development of astronomical tables, the *Nautical Almanac*, and of instruments such as the sextant for the lunar distance method; the other came with John Harrison's invention of an accurate sea watch, the forerunner of the marine chronometer.

THE

NAUTICAL ALMANAC

AND

ASTRONOMICAL EPHEMERIS,

FOR THE YEAR 1767.

Published by ORDER of the

COMMISSIONERS OF LONGITUDE.

LONDON:

Printed by W. RICHARDSON and S. CLARK, PRINTERS;

AND SOLD BY

J. NOURSE, in the Strand, and Meff. MOUNT and PAGE, on Tower-Hill,

Bookfellers to the faid COMMISSIONERS.

M DCC LXVI.

▲ Title page of the Nautical Almanac for 1767, the first edition of this annual set of astronomical tables for navigation.

		AUGUST 1767.			[93]
		Diftances of ☽'s Center from Stars, and from ☉ eaft of her.			
Days	Stars Names.	Noon.	3 Hours.	6 Hours.	9 Hours.
		° ′ ″	° ′ ″	° ′ ″	° ′ ″
1	Antares.	43. 47. 32	42. 17. 29	40. 47. 17	39. 16. 55
2	α Aquilæ	87. 11. 41	85. 51. 51	84. 31. 52	83. 11. 44
3		76. 28. 53	75. 7. 56	73. 46. 52	72. 25. 44
4	β Capri- corni.	61. 37. 36	60. 1. 22	58. 24. 46	56. 47. 48
5		48. 37. 21	46. 58. 7	45. 18. 27	43. 38. 23
6	α Pegafi.	85. 12. 28	83. 32. 52	81. 52. 50	80. 12. 26
7		71. 44. 54	70. 2. 24	68. 19. 37	66. 36. 35
8		57. 57. 54	56. 13. 38	54. 29. 19	52. 44. 59
9		44. 4. 35	42. 21. 17	40. 38. 25	38. 56. 2
10	α Arietis.	69. 55. 50	68. 2. 58	66. 10. 4	64. 17. 9
11		54. 52. 53	53. 0. 14	51. 7. 43	49. 15. 21
12	Aldeba- ran.	72. 33. 6	70. 42. 48	68. 52. 50	67. 3. 10
13		57. 59. 35	56. 11. 56	54. 24. 42	52. 37. 52
14		43. 50. 39	42. 6. 45	40. 23. 28	38. 40. 48
15		30. 18. 7	28. 40. 6	27. 3. 8	25. 27. 21
14	The Sun.	117. 15. 50	115. 35. 49	113. 56. 11	112. 16. 54
15		104. 6. 2	102. 28. 58	100. 52. 15	99. 15. 54
16		91. 19. 30	89. 45. 15	88. 11. 20	86. 37. 47
17		78. 55. 4	77. 23. 29	75. 52. 13	74. 21. 16
18		66. 50. 54	65. 21. 38	63. 52. 38	62. 23. 56
19		55. 4. 12	53. 36. 57	52. 9. 56	50. 43. 8
20		43. 32. 26	42. 6. 54	40. 41. 33	39. 16. 22
26	Spica ♍	25. 7. 51	23. 40. 1	22. 12. 17	20. 44. 39
27	Antares.	58. 56. 22	57. 27. 42	55. 58. 57	54. 30. 8
28		47. 5. 15	45. 36. 2	44. 6. 44	42. 37. 19
29		35. 8. 39	33. 38. 31	32. 8. 14	30. 37. 46
30	α Aquilæ	79. 37. 9	78. 17. 49	76. 58. 26	75. 39. 0
31		69. 1. 23	67. 41. 53	66. 22. 27	65. 3. 7

▲ One of the tables from the Nautical Almanac for 1767.

Measuring longitude by the Moon

The work of the 5th Astronomer Royal, Nevil Maskelyne, significantly improved the use of astronomical methods of longitude determination at sea. To determine a ship's longitude from the Moon and the Sun or a nearby bright star – the lunar distance method – navigators needed to measure the angle between these precisely and consult accurate tables of the predicted position of the Moon and certain bright stars for the entire duration of the voyage, which in some cases lasted one or more years, to help calculate their position. Having tested the lunar distance method for himself on a voyage to the South Atlantic island of St Helena in 1761, Maskelyne was convinced that he could make the technique available to others. New mathematical models of the Moon's complex motion by scholars such as Leonhard Euler and Tobias Mayer also helped improve the calculations. At the Royal Observatory, Maskelyne worked with his assistant to collect and record the required astronomical data to predict the Moon's changing position for the year ahead. These papers were distributed to a network of mathematically trained human 'computers' who corrected and adjusted the data into a more useable format before returning it to Greenwich. Maskelyne then compiled the data to create the first *Nautical Almanac* for the year 1767.

Using these tables and Maskelyne's helpful handbook, *The British Mariner's Guide* (1763), the trained navigator could now calculate his longitude at sea by measuring the Moon's position ('distance') and adjusting it with data from the *Nautical Almanac* to determine the time at Greenwich for comparison with the ship's local time. Over subsequent decades, navigators began to rely on the *Nautical Almanac* and other tools such as the marine sextant and marine chronometer to help them determine longitude at sea. The marine sextant was developed in the late 1750s during trials of astronomical methods of navigation. It became the standard navigational tool for the next 200 years. By the early 19th century, these instruments began to be produced in larger numbers, making them more affordable and widely used. Similarly, navigators were routinely trained in how to use these instruments and techniques.

▶ *Sextant, by Jesse Ramsden, about 1797.*

John Harrison's timekeepers

With his unconventional approach to clock making, John Harrison introduced significant improvements to timekeepers and created the world's first timekeepers to calculate longitude at sea. Harrison was not the first to attempt this; the idea had been formulated as early as 1530, but despite several attempts, nobody had managed to make a practical marine timekeeper. The development of the longcase pendulum clock in 1656 offered a more accurate type of timekeeper that, with temperature compensation, could keep time to a second per day, but the motion on board ships caused them to stop. Portable watches also existed at this time but with an error of up to 15 minutes per day, they lacked the accuracy required at sea.

▲ John Harrison, print after a portrait by Thomas King, with H3 in the background and H4 on the table, 1768.

Harrison was a joiner and self-taught clockmaker based in Lincolnshire. Using his knowledge of carpentry, he created clocks made almost entirely of wood rather than conventional materials such as brass and steel. His innovative approach led him to create precision timekeepers, achieving unprecedented accuracy and reliability. Over ten years after the Longitude Act of 1714, Harrison turned his attention to adapting his precision timekeepers to the marine environment.

In 1735, he presented his first marine timekeeper, now known as H1, to the Board of Longitude. Encouraged by its good performance during an unofficial sea trial to Lisbon, the Board awarded Harrison funding to produce two more timekeepers, as Harrison believed he could improve his design. H2, completed in 1739, contained additional developments but Harrison discovered a fundamental flaw and immediately started to work on a third design, H3, in 1740. Though he completed it within five years, Harrison spent a total of 19 years refining and adjusting the instrument. Realising his first three timekeepers would never achieve the accuracy he desired, he radically changed his approach and constructed a new timepiece based on the principles of a portable watch. At the time, watches were thought to be inaccurate and unsuitable for this task. Harrison persevered with his ideas and in 1759 he presented H4 to the Board of Longitude to undergo a trial at sea in an attempt to secure the longitude reward. To win the reward, the method had to establish the longitude within certain limits of accuracy on a voyage between the West Indies and back. However, the Board also stipulated that the method had to be practically available to all navigators. In terms of accuracy, H4 performed extraordinarily well, but as this experimental and complicated design took six years to make, at a cost of £500, it did not meet the Board's requirements of practicality. With sextants and the *Nautical Almanac* available for £20, H4 was thought to be too expensive and time consuming to replicate. Harrison had proved that timekeepers could provide a solution at sea, but the means to do so were not yet established.

Did you know?

H1 contains over 1,443 parts and weighs 74 lb!

▶ *H4 – and we have a winner! Harrison's fourth marine timekeeper, 1759.*

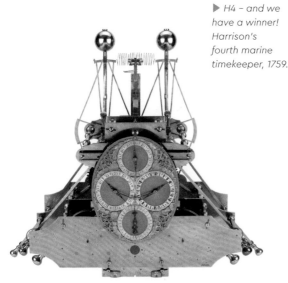

▲ *H1 – at last, a clock that keeps time at sea! 1736.*

Find out more

Take a look at the 'Time for the Navy' gallery to see more of our collection of marine chronometers.

The Greenwich Time-Ball

The Time-Ball was installed on the eastern turret of Flamsteed House to provide an accurate time signal to ships in dock and on the river so that navigators could rate their marine chronometers. This visual method of displaying accurate time was the brainchild of Captain Robert Wauchope R.N. (1788–1862), who in 1829 successfully trialled the idea in Portsmouth. Understanding the need for such a service, the 6th Astronomer Royal John Pond installed an improved version at Greenwich in 1833.

The Greenwich signal has three stages: at 12.55 p.m. the ball is hoisted halfway up the mast, where it remains until 12.58 p.m. when it is raised to the top, alerting people that the signal is imminent; the ball then drops at precisely 1.00 p.m. Initially, the ball was hoisted and dropped manually by an assistant who watched the second hand of a mechanical clock. From 1852 to the mid-1900s, the new Shepherd electrical clock system activated the dropping of the ball (see page 28). Today, the operation of the Time-Ball is entirely automatic and a radio-controlled quartz clock controls the timing of the signal.

▲ *Illustration of the time ball mechanism within turret of Flamsteed House, in the* Illustrated London News, *November 1844.*

The 'Time and Greenwich' Gallery

Up until the mid-19th century, individual towns across Britain kept local time. For most people, life was regulated by the Sun, and accuracy, as required by navigators at sea, was of little importance. Public and domestic clocks were set to local mean time by applying the equation of time to apparent solar time, as shown by a sundial. Astronomers created mean ('average') time to smooth out the variation in solar time caused by the Earth's tilt on its axis and its elliptical orbit. Local communities were thus regulated by mean solar time and across Britain, only towns located on the same meridian would keep the same time. From coast to coast, time varied between cities with places in the east, such as Yarmouth, seven minutes ahead of Greenwich, while those further west, such as Penzance, some 22 minutes behind.

Greenwich Mean Time (GMT)

Such variations in local time from east to west made little difference to people's lives until the development of the railway networks. With each town on the railway line following its own local time, the organisation of railway timetables during the 1830s became chaotic and potentially dangerous. During the mid-19th century, each railway network in the United States kept its own timetable based on the local time of each company's home station, creating over 60 different time standards. A traveller journeying from Maine to California would have had to change their watch at least 20 times during the trip to ensure making a connection. In Britain, the time variation was less extreme, but still necessary. Railway passengers travelling from London to Liverpool had to put their watches back 12 minutes on arrival to compensate for travelling from east to west. But by the 1840s, most railway companies had adopted Greenwich Mean Time (GMT) as their standard time across the network, irrespective of local time. With growing demand for the supply of GMT, 7th Astronomer Royal George Biddell Airy saw an opportunity for the Observatory to extend its time distribution beyond the Navy.

▶ *This gold traveller's watch has two minute-hands. One can be set to Greenwich Mean Time and the other to any particular local time. The inner back of the watch is engraved with various places and their time differences. Benjamin Lewis Vulliamy, date unknown.*

The Shepherd Gate Clock

In 1851 at the famous Great Exhibition held in Hyde Park, Charles Shepherd, a London clockmaker, installed one of the world's first ever 'master-and-slave' clock systems. It consisted of a central 'master clock' which sent regular electrical impulses to a number of simple ancillary 'slave' dials. This was far cheaper than having good quality clocks in every room of a large office building or factory. Airy saw the potential advantages of such a system and ordered one to be made for the Royal Observatory in Greenwich. The Shepherd Gate Clock is mounted on the wall outside the gate to the courtyard to the Royal Observatory, which was installed in 1852. The Gate Clock is one of the slave dials operated by the Master Clock and was the first clock to display GMT for the benefit of the public. The Master Clock also operated clocks in various other parts of the Observatory. One displayed time in the Chronometer Room, another in the Computing Room and another in Airy's own residence. Signals from this clock were also distributed via telegraph wires to synchronise clocks at London railway stations and to drop time balls at Charing Cross, Deal and Edinburgh. Airy wrote of this system; 'I cannot help but feel a satisfaction in thinking that the Royal Observatory is thus quietly contributing to the punctuality of business through a large portion of this busy country'.

▶ *Slave clock connected to the Shepherd Master Clock, which was installed at the Royal Observatory in 1852. By Charles Shepherd. Image below shows the clock c.1890.*

THE CLOCK, ROYAL OBSERVATORY, GREENWICH

By the mid-1850s, the necessity for standard time in Britain became the subject of heated debate. Many people, particularly those in the north and west of the country, resented the imposition of time from Greenwich. Since the move towards a standard time was spearheaded by the railways, some writers referred to the move as 'railway aggression', thinking that the new proposal was just some clever ploy aimed at the common man by the government and big business. Despite this protest, by 1855, 98% of all the public clocks in Britain were set to GMT. Many of the timekeepers you see on display in the galleries were used by the Observatory to distribute GMT throughout the UK.

Did you know?

This clock was used as the first time standard for the BBC's 'six-pip' time signal. From 1924, the BBC converted the electrical impulses sent by the clock down a telephone wire into audio pips for radio broadcasts.

▶ *Astronomical regulator, Edward John Dent & Co. 1874.*

◀ *Electrically-corrected dial clock, the Standard Time and Telephone Company, about 1890.*

Ruth Belville (1854–1943)

Ruth Belville, known as the Greenwich Time Lady, supplied GMT to London chronometer makers using a John Arnold pocket chronometer. Her father John Henry Belville started the service in the 1830s while he was working at the Observatory. Each week he travelled across London to subscribers who used this measure of GMT to rate their chronometers. Despite competition from electrical time distribution systems in later years, John's widow Maria took over the service on his death in 1856, continuing until she was 81 years old. From 1892 her daughter Ruth took over until her retirement in 1940 at the age of 86. Once a week, Ruth would call at the Observatory to have 'Arnold' rated, after which she would travel to some 40 or 50 addresses in London. Here she would be greeted by her clients: 'Good morning, Miss Belville, how's Arnold today?' to which she would reply:

▲ *Ruth Belville in front of the Shepherd Gate Clock, 1908.*

'Arnold's four seconds fast today'. By the time of her retirement multiple time-regulation services were widely available. These included speaking clocks and radio signals, of which the famous BBC six pips is possibly the best known.

Keeping in sync

Established in the late 19th century, the Standard Time and Telephone Company distributed time by means of synchronisation. Subscribers would receive hourly time-synchronisation signals through overhead wires. In 1904, to push the market for their business, the new director promoted legislation that public clocks should denote GMT, by synchronisation. Clock communities protested as their weekly winding and correction services would have been made obsolete with the automatic system. Fortunately for these communities, the law did not pass, although later technologies eventually made their services redundant.

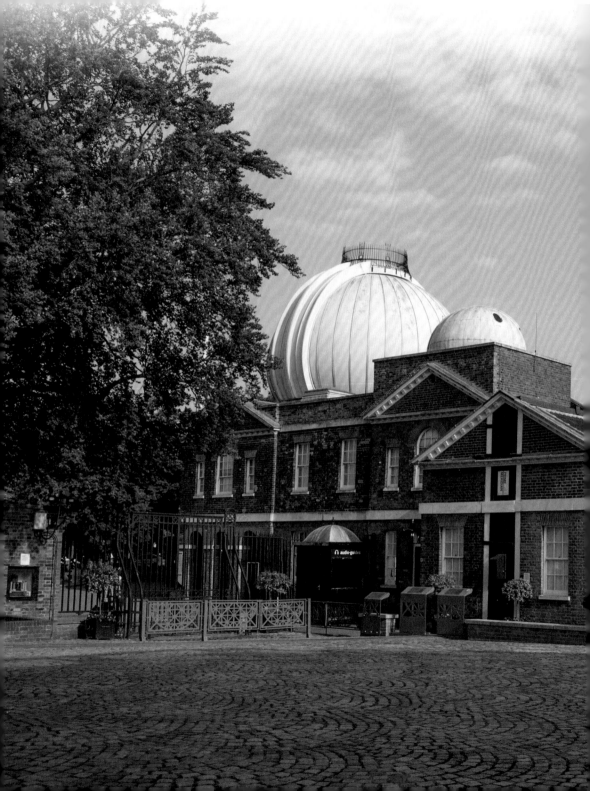

The Meridian Observatory

The Meridian Observatory was the heart of astronomical work at Greenwich for much of the Royal Observatory's history. Different generations of Astronomers Royal created their own meridians and bought new instruments, each one a few steps further east, culminating with the installation of the Airy Transit Circle in 1850. Despite the changing technology and enhanced optics, the core principle remained the same over the centuries: the astronomer would measure the height of the stars and other celestial objects above the horizon as they crossed the observer's meridian (north-south line). These observations were essential for timekeeping and for improving the mapping of the stars to aid navigation at sea.

Observing began at this part of the site in 1676, when the first Astronomer Royal had a sextant house and quadrant house built at the western end. By the time his successor Edmond Halley arrived in 1720, Flamsteed's building was subsiding down the hill. Halley commissioned a new building in 1725 to accommodate a better mural quadrant and accurate timekeeper (regulator) supplied by the prestigious London clockmaker George Graham.

◀ *Flamsteed's sextant house and mural quadrant, as depicted in his posthumous star catalogue, the* Historia Coelestis Britannicae, *1725.*

▲ *The Royal Observatory from the south-east, watercolour, artist unknown, about 1770. The Meridian Observatory is on the right with the distinctive gap in the roof.*

It was in 1749 that James Bradley, Halley's successor, was given money to build a 'New Observatory'. As well as housing meridian instruments, the new building included a bedroom for the astronomer's assistant on the first floor with a calculating room and library below.

Much of the astronomical work at Greenwich took place in the Meridian Observatory. The Astronomer Royal and, even more so, his assistant would spend many hours here recording the position of the stars and other bodies, with further hours spent turning the observations into data that could be used by others. It was arduous and taxing work. Thomas Evans, an assistant from 1796 to 1798, complained that,

> *'Nothing can exceed the tediousness and ennui of the life the assistant leads in this place, excluded from all society, except, perhaps, that of a poor mouse which may occasionally sally forth from a hole in the wall ... Here forlorn, he spends days, weeks, and months, in the same long wearisome computations, without a friend to shorten the tedious hours, or a soul with whom he can converse.'*

Observations were carried out from this building almost continuously until the late 1950s.

The Bradley Transit Room

By the time James Bradley became 3rd Astronomer Royal in 1742, he was already famous for discoveries such as detecting the Earth's wobble on its axis (nutation) and providing the first observational proof of the Earth's motion around the Sun, deduced from the apparent change in the position of certain stars (aberration of light).

Having overseen its construction, Bradley equipped his 'New Observatory' with an 8-ft transit instrument by renowned London instrument maker John Bird and with another regulator from George Graham. He used these to refine the data for over 3,000 stars. As the principal telescope at the Observatory, the transit instrument defined the meridian for observations from Greenwich.

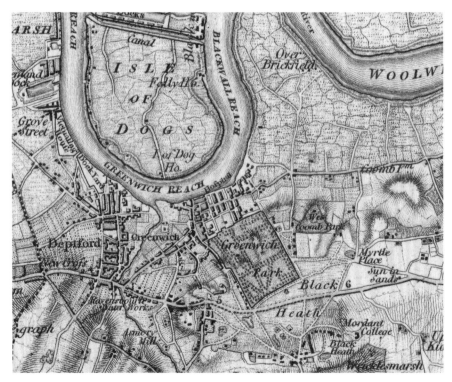

▲ *The first Ordnance Survey map, with zero degrees longitude defined by the Bradley Meridian, 1801.*

Bradley's meridian served as Britain's prime meridian until 1850, although Bird's telescope was replaced in 1816 by a new and larger transit instrument by Edward Troughton of London. During the time of the 5th Astronomer Royal, Nevil Maskelyne, this meridian was used for the *Nautical Almanac*, the astronomical tables produced by the Royal Observatory to aid navigation at sea. It was also the meridian used for the first Ordnance Survey map of Britain and is still used for their maps today.

◀ *Regulator, by George Graham, about 1750. This very accurate clock was used at the Royal Observatory for 174 years.*

▶ *Transit instrument, by Edward Troughton, 1816.*

The Airy Transit Circle

Designed by and named after George Biddell Airy, the 7th Astronomer Royal, the Airy Transit Circle consists of a 12-ft (3.7 m) long telescope mounted between two stone piers on a meridian. It was installed here in 1850 and was used for over a century to make around 600,000 observations.

After opening the roof hatches above, the astronomer sat in the pit below and looked through the eyepiece to time the precise moment at which certain stars appeared to transit the meridian. He pressed a switch that caused a sharp needle to puncture a series of pin-pricks onto a paper-covered drum that rotated in sync with signals from a nearby clock. Another astronomer would look through the microscopes on the western pier to read the finely graduated angle scale. Two collimation telescopes at each end were used to ensure the instrument's correct alignment with the meridian.

◀ Astronomers needed this set of microscopes to read the finely engraved angle scales on the Airy Transit Circle. Microscope 'P' shows the number of whole degrees while the other high-power microscopes 'A' to 'F' show the smaller divisions.

▲ *The Airy Transit Circle at Greenwich, as shown in E. Dunkin's* The Midnight Sky *(1891).*
Sitting in the pit underneath, the astronomer timed the stars as they crossed the meridian.

The Prime Meridian of the World

The Airy Transit Circle was designated as the defining instrument of the world's prime meridian (0° longitude) in 1884. For latitude, we can rely on the equator as the natural zero line from which to measure our position within the northern and southern hemispheres. Unfortunately, there is no natural prime meridian for longitude and so people have used various meridians, from the meridian passing through the Canary Islands used by the Ancient Greeks to other meridians defined by national observatories in Paris, Berlin and Stockholm.

  With no international agreement on the choice of a single prime meridian, many different meridians were used for maps and tables of astronomical data. By the mid-19th century, this was impractical for international trade and the growing spread of telegraph and railway networks. In 1884, delegates at the International Meridian Conference in Washington, D.C., recommended that 'the meridian passing through the centre of the transit instrument at the Observatory of Greenwich' should be adopted as the Prime Meridian of the World. They also recommended that the universal day for the world should begin at the moment of mean midnight on the Greenwich meridian – the basis for the time zone system. Greenwich became the home of the Prime Meridian and the origin of Greenwich Mean Time (GMT).

▶ Looking south along the Meridian Line.

◀ Delegates of the International Meridian Conference, Washington D.C., 1884.

The 'Time and Society' Gallery

This gallery examines the role of timekeeping in our everyday lives.
At home and at work, in our personal lives and across societies, we
have made timekeepers to coordinate and track the passing of the years.
Explore the objects in this gallery to see how this has been done in
different times and cultures.

Natural timekeepers

For centuries people have measured time by the apparent motion of the
Sun, Moon and stars across the sky. Skilled mathematicians and craftspeople
created instruments that could represent and quantify these changing
shadows and patterns. These were known as natural timekeepers.

Portable sundial: *Held taut between
two pieces of the ivory, the string on this
17th-century diptych dial casts the Sun's
shadow onto the surrounding hour scale.
The angle of the string can be adjusted to
the latitudes of the listed European cities.
Just like a smartphone today, it has a range of
functions, from calculating the date of Easter
to telling the time by the light of the Full Moon.*

◀ *Diptych dial, Thomas Durcher, 17th century.*

Looking north: *Known as a nocturnal,
this instrument uses the apparent rotation
of the stars around the north star
(Polaris) to measure time at night.
The user would set the instrument
for the date, view Polaris through the
central hole and then align the long
arm with the stars of Ursa Major. Some
versions featured jagged teeth to help
the user feel the hour scale in the dark.
Nocturnals were usually made of boxwood
and were popular during the 17th century.*

▶ *Nocturnal, unknown maker, 17th century.*

Did you know?

We still use sundial words in our language today. The terms a.m. and p.m., referring to morning and afternoon, are abbreviations of ante meridiem (before the Sun crosses meridian) and post meridiem (after the Sun crosses the meridian). At 12 noon, the Sun is at its highest point in the sky and directly over the meridian. It is therefore neither 'a.m.' or 'p.m.'.

Bang on time: This type of novelty sundial was popular in the 19th century. At noon, the Sun's rays are focused through the magnifying lens onto the fuse of a small cannon. The resulting explosion signals the time.

▲ *Cannon dial, Victor Chevalier, 1834–1843.*

Rotating stars: *Developed by Ancient Greek and Islamic mathematicians, the astrolabe is a complex astronomical calculator. Holding the instrument vertically, astronomers used sighting vanes on the back to estimate the height of the Sun or stars above the horizon. They then used the specific alignment and rotation of the front discs to calculate the time. Made in 1575, this sophisticated instrument was an expensive timekeeper that few people could afford or use.*

▶ *Astrolabe, Georg Hartmann, 1548.*

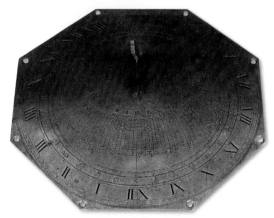

Setting the format: *Instrument maker Elias Allen and mathematician William Oughtred collaborated to create this sophisticated type of sundial around 1640. Horizontal sundials such as this have 12 noon at the top with the morning hours on the left and afternoon hours on the right. We still use this layout on our mechanical clocks today.*

◀ *Horizontal pedestal dial, Elias Allen, c.1640.*

Mechanical timekeepers

'Time is money ... time is precious ... time must not be wasted'. Our perception and use of time has changed dramatically as our society has become more urban and industrialised. Mechanical timekeepers adapted and evolved to keep up with changing perspectives and use. These are just a few examples of the different types of timekeepers and how they have influenced our lives.

Time is money: *Made by the 'father of English clockmaking', Thomas Tompion, this longcase clock once adorned the residence of the Earl of Strafford. Time was indeed money, as only the wealthy could afford to purchase such a luxurious work of art.*

▶ *Eight-day grande sonnerie parquetry longcase clock, Thomas Tompion, 1682.*

One for the road: *Before the advent of electric time distribution, and for those that could not afford the luxury of a Tompion timekeeper, these large dial clocks were often found in taverns, inns and other public places to provide the right time. They were especially prominent during the 18th century, when travelling by stagecoach became more common and travellers used these public clocks to set their watches.*

◀ *Tavern clock, George Bennett, Greenwich 1802–1811.*

Working 9 to 5: *Our use of time changed dramatically during the late 19th century as Greenwich Mean Time increasingly shaped work, life and leisure. Factories relied on slave dials to regulate workers' productivity and breaks. These types of slave dials were common in factories and offices.*

▲ *Slave dial, Synchronome Co. Ltd, 1920s.*

Time travel:
This time recorder is housed inside a tamper-proof metal case for exterior use. Time recorders like this were once installed along bus routes in the early 20th century. Bus drivers would use punch cards to 'clock on' at various points, enabling inspectors to check their timekeeping.

◀ *Roadside time recording clock, Gledhill Brook, 1920s.*

Fine tuning: *Watch manufacturers Bulova introduced the world's first electronic watch, the 'Accutron'. It is controlled by a tiny tuning-fork vibrating 360 times per second, maintained by a transistorised electronic circuit and a battery lasting about a year. In 1964 the Accutron was chosen to be buried in a 5,000-year time capsule on the grounds of the New York World's Fair as an example of one of the most innovative objects invented in the preceding 25 years.*

◀ *Bulova 'Accutron' tuning-fork wristwatch, Bulova, c.1969.*

The Great Equatorial Telescope

The installation of the Great Equatorial Telescope in 1893 marked a turning point for the Royal Observatory. A decade earlier, the 8th Astronomer Royal, William Christie, had realised that other observatories were building bigger and better telescopes. He persuaded the Admiralty to replace the existing 12.8-inch (32.5 cm) telescope with this larger version, thus keeping the Observatory at the forefront of research into the nature of the universe, while continuing with more practical work related to timekeeping and navigation. The main lens at the end of the telescope is 28 inches (71 cm) in diameter and collects over 10,000 times more light than the average eye. The metal structure supporting the telescope is called an equatorial mount – hence the name 'Great Equatorial'. This type of mount tilts the telescope, so it can turn in a plane parallel with the Earth's equator and stay firmly fixed on the stars and planets as they appear to move, ideal for long exposure photographs. The telescope was used for observing double stars and for spectroscopy (analysing starlight) until 1947 when it was transferred to the Observatory's new, smog-free, country site at Herstmonceux in Sussex. It was later re-installed here as a museum piece and public telescope during the early 1970s.

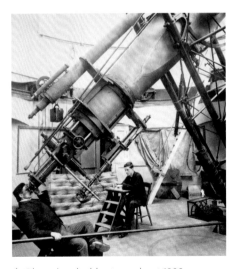

▲ *Observing double stars, about 1900.*

▲ *The Great Equatorial Telescope, viewed from the interior of the dome at night.*

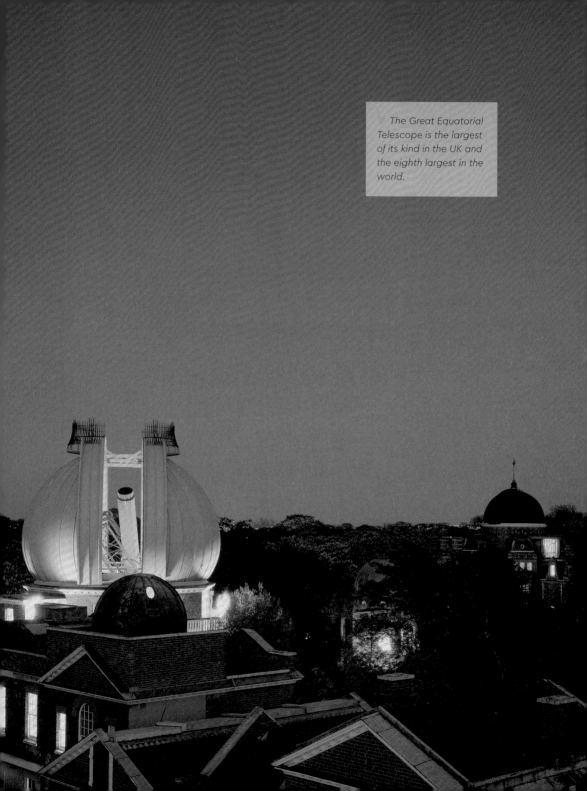

The Great Equatorial Telescope is the largest of its kind in the UK and the eighth largest in the world.

The 'Time for the Navy' Gallery

By the 1820s the Royal Navy began to demand more and more sophisticated equipment to improve safety at sea. The 'Time for the Navy' gallery examines how the Royal Navy drove timekeeping technology, and how the Royal Observatory coordinated the servicing, repair and testing of all the Royal Navy's chronometers.

Development of the marine chronometer

Despite the fact that the numerous trials of John Harrison's timekeepers had proved the possibility of making a reliable timekeeper, his inventions were still largely experimental and expensive. To receive his share of the reward, Harrison had to hand over his designs to the Board of Longitude to prove that his ideas could be reproduced. Watchmaker Larcum Kendall was commissioned to reproduce H4 but it cost the Board of Longitude £500. In order to make this method of finding longitude 'practicable and useful at sea', watchmakers needed to devise a way to manufacture marine timekeepers more quickly and less expensively.

Towards industrialisation

John Arnold (1736–1799) contributed significantly to the development of the modern marine chronometer. By simplifying Harrison's designs and building on technologies devised by French watchmakers, Arnold created the first affordable accurate timekeeper a few years later. He presented his work to the Board of Longitude in 1771 and estimated that his timekeeper could be produced for just 60 guineas, about an eighth of the cost of H4. The Royal Society commissioned three of these timekeepers and they were used on Captain Cook's second voyage to the southern hemisphere on board HMS *Resolution* (1772–75). Though they did not perform very well, Arnold's further improvements led to his domination of the chronometer market for the remainder of the century.

▲ *'Arnold no. 23' with its original octagonal case, John Arnold, 1784.*

What's in a name?

This watch, made in 1778 and known as 'Arnold No. 36', performed so accurately on a trial at Greenwich that it was the first timepiece that came to be known as a 'chronometer'. Alexander Dalrymple, later the first Hydrographer of the Navy, declared that it should be 'named CHRONOMETER [since] so valuable a Machine deserves to be known by a Name, instead of a Definition'.

▶ 'Arnold no. 36', the first official chronometer, John Arnold, 1778.

Chronometers for all

Thomas Earnshaw (1749–1829) followed Arnold's pioneering work. His great achievement was to standardise the form of the chronometer. He also introduced a series of new manufacturing methods paired with rigid quality controls, which meant his watches could be reproduced quickly, cheaply and in large numbers. By 1800, Earnshaw had created the modern marine chronometer, a design that barely changed in the following 150 years.

Chronometer trials

The Royal Observatory played a significant role in providing the Navy with reliable chronometers at sea following its initial development in the 18th century. By the turn of the 19th century, chronometers were increasingly requested and used by

▲ 'Earnshaw 512', the marine chronometer as we know it today, Thomas Earnshaw, c.1801.

Royal Navy captains, and the Royal Observatory oversaw the testing and distribution of these instruments. John Pond, the 6th Astronomer Royal, superintended the growing stock of government-owned chronometers. He was tasked with purchasing, issuing and managing chronometers intended for use by the Admiralty. Equipped with the most accurate clocks of the day, the Observatory was the ideal place for testing the accuracy of marine chronometers.

Chronometer rates

Chronometers did not keep perfect time but would gain or lose time each day. Staff at the Royal Observatory would test the chronometers to establish exactly how much a chronometer gained or lost per day. They recorded this on a rating certificate that was issued with the chronometer to a naval captain. However, it was well-known that on board a ship the chronometer would alter its rate, though the reasons why were still being investigated. John Pond built the Greenwich Time-Ball so that mariners waiting on the River Thames could check for a change in the rate before heading out to sea (see page 26).

Encouraging excellence

To encourage chronometer makers to further improve their instruments, the Observatory initiated annual trials at Greenwich in 1822. From the Admiralty's point of view, these Premium Trials were intended to improve the accuracy of chronometers by buying top quality chronometers at premium prices of £300, £200 and (from 1829) £100. This secured the best instruments for use in the Navy. For the chronometer makers, winning the annual trial was a way of gaining prestige and access to a market dominated by Arnold and Earnshaw The premium trials ended in 1835, as the trials had achieved their aim and greatly improved the instruments..

Under the 7th Astronomer Royal, George Biddell Airy, the Greenwich Trials were reinstated in 1840. No premiums were rewarded, but the best chronometers were purchased for the Navy and the makers gained the right to describe themselves as 'Maker to the Admiralty'. Thus throughout the 19th century, the Royal Observatory provided a scientific service in testing the accuracy of chronometers. For over 100 years this essential testing, which included heating the chronometers in an oven to simulate tropical temperatures, took place in the two rooms below the Great Equatorial Telescope. Getting the very best performance from chronometers became highly scientific, and a very profitable business, and the 19th century was a period of intense competition among makers producing these cutting-edge navigational devices.

▲ *One of the Chronometer Rooms, on the first floor of the Observatory, where the chronometers and deck watches were tested. The ovens can just be seen on the right.*

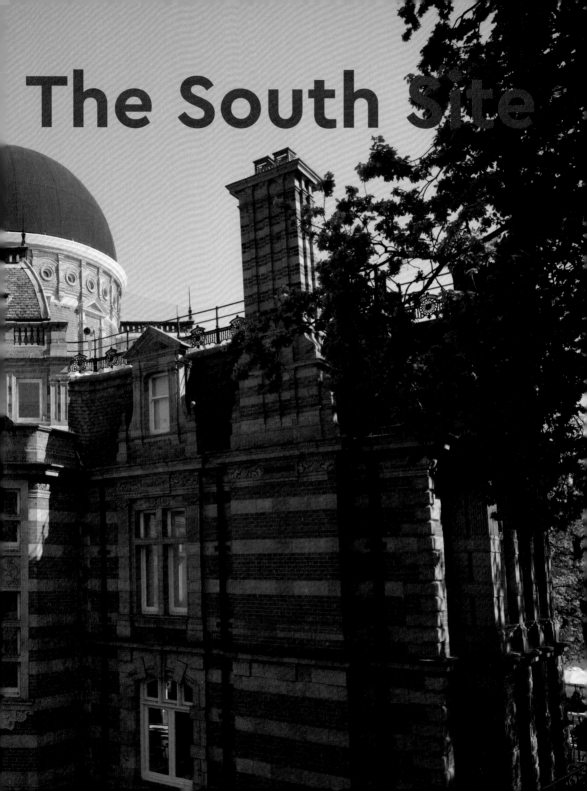

The South Site

New century, new sciences

During the early 19th century, astronomers at the Observatory began to expand their work beyond simply recording the positions of the stars. To help them understand how changes in air pressure and temperature affected their instruments and observations, the astronomers started to collect meteorological data. Similarly, collecting data about the Earth's magnetic field helped them determine whether magnetic compasses used for navigation on new iron-clad ships could be affected by these changing forces. As the site became increasingly crowded with more instruments and staff, successive Astronomers Royal petitioned the Royal Park for extra land and the Observatory site gradually expanded southwards.

Magnetic and meteorological observations

In the 1830s the Observatory site was almost doubled in order to accommodate the new Magnet House. This cruciform building was specifically constructed of materials such as wooden planks and brass nails to avoid any interference with the sensitive magnetic and electrical instruments. The Observatory became part of a network of institutions across Europe that kept meticulous records to document patterns of change within the Earth's magnetic field. This research became increasingly important as people began to rely on new technologies such as electricity and telegraphy that were affected by these magnetic fluctuations.

Every few hours, assistants at Greenwich measured the tiny movement of sensitive magnets positioned within Magnet House. To avoid disturbing the instruments, they used a small telescope positioned in the centre of the cruciform building to observe the magnets from a distance. It was time-consuming work and the 7th Astronomer Royal George Biddell Airy soon invested in new photographic technology to take automatic pictures of the readings. The assistants also took recordings from a rooftop platform of meteorological instruments, sending the data to newspapers and other observatories.

By the 1890s, the sensitive work of the Magnet House was under threat from interference caused by the iron and steel frame of the emerging New Physical Observatory, now known as the South Building. The instruments were relocated to a new site within Greenwich Park and Magnet House itself was demolished in 1917. Today the site is occupied by a 45-ton truncated cone that houses the dome of the Peter Harrison Planetarium. Made from approximately 250 pieces of bronze welded together, this prize-winning cone is tilted 51.5° to match the latitude of Greenwich, and lies parallel to the historic prime meridian.

▼ *The Observatory in the late 19th century, taken from the south, showing the wooden Magnet House surrounded by shelters containing meteorological instruments.*

◀ Bomb damage to the Altazimuth Pavilion in the Second World War, during which essential work and expensive telescopes were moved away from Greenwich.

▶ The restored Altazimuth Pavilion today. The gilded weather vane, which depicts Halley's comet, can be seen at the top.

The Altazimuth Pavilion

This perfectly formed brick and terracotta building was named after the type of telescope that was originally installed within it during the 1890s. Supported on a robust brick pier rising up through the centre of the building, the Altazimuth telescope was designed to be tilted vertically (altitude) or rotated around the horizon (azimuth). It was used to measure the position of the Moon during the first and last weeks of its monthly cycle when it was difficult to observe on the meridian.

Astronomer Andrew Crommelin (1865–1939) led the team working at the Altazimuth Pavilion until his retirement in 1927. With his colleague Philip Cowell, he was famous for successfully predicting the return of Halley's Comet in 1910. Crommelin was aided by a few young assistants who were keen to gain experience before progressing onto larger telescopes. One assistant, Frank Dyson, went on to become the 9th Astronomer Royal, in 1910.

The last observations were made in 1929 and the telescope was subsequently dismantled in 1940. The Pavilion suffered a direct bomb hit on the night of 21–22 October 1940 and was later rebuilt as a public park shelter after the war. Today it is used as an exhibition space and as a working observatory upstairs.

The Annie Maunder Astrographic Telescope (AMAT)

In 2018, the Altazimuth Pavilion was restored as a functional observatory once again, thanks to a successful fundraising appeal. The new collection of telescopes that have been installed in the dome are named after Annie Maunder (1868–1947), in recognition of her pioneering work as an astrophotographer.

Annie Maunder (née Scott Dill Russell) was one of the first female astronomers employed at Greenwich. She was recruited as a 'lady computer' in September 1891 to help convert the raw astronomical observational data into a more useable format. She was also assigned to the Solar Department and took daily photographs of the Sun to record its changing cycle of sunspots. A few years later, Annie was obliged to resign from her post when she married her colleague

▲ Annie Maunder was also one of the first women to be elected as Fellows of the Royal Astronomical Society, in 1916.

Edward Walter Maunder in December 1895, according to the conventions of the day. Undeterred, she continued to develop new photographic techniques for recording eclipses and travelled the world with Walter to capture incredible images of the Sun's outer atmosphere.

Both Annie and Walter were keen to share their knowledge and enthusiasm for astronomy with others and the Annie Maunder Astrographic Telescope (AMAT) continues their legacy today. It is used for public and school engagement through live-stream events online and occasional tours of the telescopes. These instruments are used with a variety of CCD cameras, special filters and other accessories to carry out different observing programmes, from solar photography to spectroscopy.

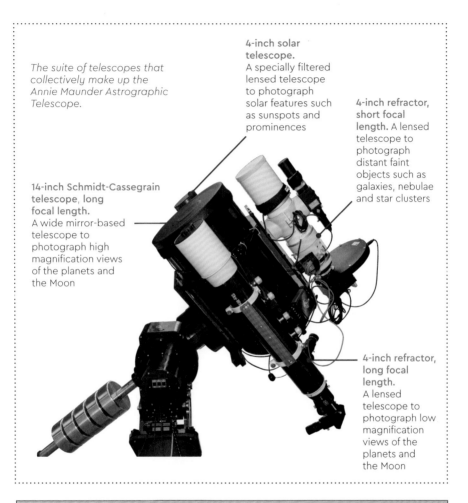

The suite of telescopes that collectively make up the Annie Maunder Astrographic Telescope.

4-inch solar telescope. A specially filtered lensed telescope to photograph solar features such as sunspots and prominences

4-inch refractor, short focal length. A lensed telescope to photograph distant faint objects such as galaxies, nebulae and star clusters

14-inch Schmidt-Cassegrain telescope, long focal length. A wide mirror-based telescope to photograph high magnification views of the planets and the Moon

4-inch refractor, long focal length. A lensed telescope to photograph low magnification views of the planets and the Moon

Find out more...

You can explore the Annie Maunder Astrographic Telescope and see some of the spectacular images taken here at Greenwich on a guided tour. The tours combine an insight into the astronomy of the 19th century with what it's like to be an astronomer in the 21st century. Visit our website for more details.

The South Building

Significant building work took place in the 1890s in response to the growing demands of astrophotography. The New Physical Observatory, shortly after known simply as the South Building, originally contained large equatorial telescopes and offices for the astronomers, assistants and (human) computers, as well as stores, records, workshops and darkrooms. By the late 19th century, astrophotography had become an essential part of the Observatory's output and the much-needed building offered space for the increasing number of photographic plates produced on a daily basis. The building was crowned by a dome that housed two large telescopes, both donated by the wealthy amateur astronomer Sir Henry Thompson. Designed by Admiralty architect William Crisp, the building is highly ornate with a series of terracotta tiles around its exterior that commemorate the

▼ The South Building under construction during the 1890s.

names of the first seven Astronomers Royal, along with the names of other prominent astronomers, mathematicians, clockmakers and instrument makers significant to the Observatory's history. In the 1890s, this design was a confident statement of the Observatory's ambition to celebrate its contribution to British astronomy and remain at the forefront of astronomical research.

▶ *The weather vane in the shape of Henry VIII's flagship, Henri Grace à Dieu, or Great Harry.*

Did you know?

This sculpture, which can be found on the north-west side of the South Building, shows Astronomia, the Greek muse of astronomy, balancing the Sun and Moon in her hands against a background arch of zodiac signs. It was made by the artist William J. Neatby, who worked at the Doulton ceramic factory in Lambeth and who is mainly remembered for his decorative ceramic work that adorns the meat hall at Harrods, completed in 1902.

Despite the confident expansion of the site at the start of the 20th century, it was becoming increasingly difficult to observe effectively at Greenwich. As both London and its Thames-side industry expanded, the astronomers found their work hindered by smoke and light pollution. New train lines also caused problems, first with vibrations and then, after the electrification of the Southern Railway in 1923, with serious interference to magnetic observations. This meant the work had to be moved to a new site at Abinger in Surrey. Observing conditions continued to deteriorate and it fell to 10th Astronomer Royal Harold Spencer Jones to plan a move. It was delayed by the Second World War but from 1948 onwards various departments were resettled 60 miles south at Herstmonceux Castle in Sussex as the 'Royal Greenwich Observatory' (RGO). Under this title it moved again to Cambridge in 1990 but was finally closed eight years later as astronomers began to use larger telescopes in better climates abroad.

At Greenwich, the Admiralty initially used the site for accommodation until the Observatory became part of the National Maritime Museum in 1953. The oldest part of the site, Flamsteed House, was opened fully to the public by 1960 with additional buildings restored and reopened by the mid-1970s.

Current and future astronomy

Today the South Building contains the Weller Astronomy Galleries that bring modern astronomy to life. Through a combination of historic artefacts, hands-on interactives and digital media, visitors can explore the ideas and technology behind the big topics in astronomy today, from black holes and supernovae to extra-solar planets and the age of the Universe. The Peter Harrison Planetarium offers a range of shows, from astronomer-led tours of the night sky to fly-by cinematic tours of the universe, views of our neighbours in the Solar System or the cosmic adventures of Space Ted for younger visitors. The temporary gallery on the lower level offers a changing programme of image-rich displays on contemporary topics. Visit our website for more details.

The Royal Observatory also contributes to modern astronomy through its extensive programme of workshops and activities for schools, teacher training schemes and evening classes, accompanied by a dedicated set of digital resources online. By training and inspiring the next generation of scientists it is actively helping to ensure that the future of astronomy will be as exhilarating and surprising as its past.

The South Building, and the cone of the Peter Harrison Planetarium.

Explore more at Royal Museums Greenwich

There's plenty more to see and do at Royal Museums Greenwich. Our Museums are all within easy walking distance of each other, and together they offer a culture-filled, fun day out for all ages.

Learning at the Royal Observatory, Greenwich

A year-round programme of activities for all ages explores the collections, site and themes of the Observatory. There are study courses, including GCSE Astronomy, opportunities for observation with the Great Equatorial Telescope, and a wide range of conferences, lectures, workshops, performances and tours focusing on history and modern science.

Support

The valuable support of our Members, Patrons, donors and sponsors allows us to continue our important work through exhibitions, loans, conferences, publications, learning programmes and community initiatives. Please give generously to help us continue this vital work. You can donate at www.justgiving.com/thenmm/donate. Alternatively, you can donate by credit card by calling the Individual Giving team on +(44) 20 8312 8629, or leave a donation next time you visit. Our donation boxes are located in and around the Museum galleries. Every pound makes a difference.

Membership

If you've enjoyed your day at the Royal Observatory, Greenwich, why not consider becoming a Member? Enjoy unlimited entry to our four unique attractions: *Cutty Sark*, the Royal Observatory, National Maritime Museum and the Queen's House all year, including free entry to special exhibitions. Membership also includes invitations to private views, special Members' events, discounts in the shop, café and on public events as well as access to a lovely Members' Room and a biannual Members' magazine. Members may also purchase an annual guest pass at the Admission desk or from the Membership office. There's really no better way to enjoy the adventure. Visit rmg.co.uk/join-support/membership for more information.